Spooks

SHIVERS

Spooks

by Terry Deary

WATTS BOOKS
London · New York · Sydney

Watts Books

96 Leonard Street

London EC2A 4RH

Franklin Watts

14 Mars Road

Lane Cove

NSW

UK ISBN: 0 7496 2202 4

Dewey Decimal Classification 133·1

Editor: Rosemary McCormick

Designer: Mike Davis, Ian Probert

Author: Terry Deary

Cover Artist: Terry Oakes

Line Illustrator: Terry Oakes

Contents

Introduction   7

1. The Croglin Vampire   9

2. Jack-o-Lantern   23

3. The House in Portman Square   33

4. The Ghost Hunter   45

5. The Family Witch   57

6. Watery Grave   69

7. Beware Ticonderoga!   81

The following titles are also available:

Mystery

Terror

Disaster

Introduction

Have you ever met a ghost? Would you like to meet a ghost?

A lot of people think they'd like the excitement of meeting a real, dead spook.

But perhaps you would rather not come face to face with a phantom? If a ghost knocked on your door, are you the sort of person who would rush to lock it? (You'd be wasting your time, of course. The spook would probably open it with a skeleton key!)

Whether you're the sort of person who thinks nothin' of a moonlit graveyard, or someone who shivers at the hoot of an owl, the safest way to enjoy real ghosts is to read about them. So this book is for you.

These stories are supposed to be true. Someone, somewhere, at some time has sworn that the events described did actually happen. There are a number of facts after each story to help you make up your mind about that.

But be warned. Do not read these stories after dark! Seal off the chimney, hang garlic over your door and turn the page . . .

1. The Croglin Vampire

Most people have heard of Count Dracula, the undead creature who sleeps in his coffin by day and flies as a bat by night to suck blood from his victim's neck. But if you think that vampires haunt cold mountain castles in distant lands, then think again...

Croglin Village, Cumberland, England – 1875
Amelia Cranswell lay back in the garden chair and sighed. Life was good. Life was almost perfect in fact. The summer was fine and warm. She closed her eyes and let the soft scent of the summer flowers drift into her nostrils. Amelia laid her head back. In her pale neck a fine vein throbbed with blood.

"Penny for your thoughts, Amelia!" her brother Michael teased.

The young woman opened her eyes and smiled at him. "I was just thinking about England," she said lazily. Her voice had a soft Australian accent like her brother's. "I know father made a fortune in the gold mines of Australia. But he had to leave this place to do it. It's so peaceful, it must be worth all the gold in Australia. I'm glad we came here."

Michael laughed. "Without father's gold we wouldn't be able to live this sort of life." He waved a hand around the garden. "We couldn't have afforded Croglin Old Hall here. We couldn't afford gardeners to keep the place tidy, servants to run the house and dressmakers to keep you in those silk dresses."

Amelia poked a small pink tongue at her brother. "And you wouldn't be able to enjoy your riding and your shooting," she replied. "Admit it, you're as much in love with this corner of Cumbria as I am."

"I admit it," he shrugged.

"And you still owe me that penny you promised for my thoughts," she reminded him.

Michael called across the garden to his brother Edward who was talking to guests and admiring the blood-red roses. "Lend me a penny, brother! Our baby sister here is bleeding me dry!"

Edward smiled and threw a penny. It spun across the rich green grass and glittered like gold in the light from the copper-coloured sky. Amelia tucked it into her purse.

The air was suddenly disturbed by something black fluttering through the garden then disappearing over the wall.

"Bats from the church tower," Michael said.

He noticed that Amelia gave a shudder though the air was still warm. "You cold, sis?" he asked.

The woman shook her head. "Just a shiver . . . like someone walked over my grave."

"Let's go inside and have a drink," Michael suggested. "It's safer in there."

"Safer?" Amelia said suddenly.

Her brother frowned. "I meant to say warmer. Wonder what made me say that?"

He gave his sister his hand and helped her out of the chair. Her bulging skirts and petticoats made it hard for her to rise on her own. He led her into the house. Edward and the guests drifted after him.

The garden was left to the night and the bats.

Just before midnight Amelia closed her bedroom window. But the moonlight was so brilliant she decided to leave the shutters open. She locked her bedroom door as usual, climbed into bed and gazed out over the silver landscape.

Something moved along the top of the garden wall. Two points of red light. She rubbed her eyes. When she opened them again those points of light were at her window. They were eyes and they were staring at her. The head of her visitor was silhouetted against the moonlight so she couldn't make out if it was an animal or a human.

She felt a fear that paralysed her. She half opened her mouth but the scream wouldn't come. She willed her legs to move but they refused to obey her.

It was the scratching of nails – or claws – against the window pane that broke the spell. She threw herself out of bed and stumbled towards the door. She grasped the key in numb hands. Then came the shattering of glass and she dropped the key.

The room was in darkness now as the visitor blocked the light. Amelia fumbled for the key and snatched it up. Then she struggled to find the lock as her hand shook violently. As she looked over her shoulder, she saw the creature reach through the broken pane and unfasten the window catch. The long, bony arm threw the window open and slithered over the sill.

The red eyes were fixed on her. The stench of death filled her nostrils and sickened her. Still the scream choked in her throat. The invader grabbed her by the hair and swung her round. Now facing the moonwashed window, she could see the wrinkled face of yellow parchment, the glistening fangs and the red eyes set deep in a hairless skull. The fangs snapped at her neck and seemed to set her voice free.

Amelia screamed.

Edward and Michael tumbled from their beds and ran down the corridor. They threw themselves against the door but couldn't budge the solid oak, held with the huge brass lock. Edward leapt down the stairs, four at a time, fetched a log axe from the kitchen fireplace and beat at the lock.

When the young men finally battered their way into her room Amelia was bleeding and shocked but alive. Michael ran to the window. One shadow, darker than the rest, was snaking across the lawn. When it reached the wall, it climbed it quickly and vanished in the direction of the church.

The doctor said the wounds weren't deep and that

12

animal bites like that would soon heal.

"Animal bites?" Michael said. "These were made by a man."

"I think you're mistaken, sir," the doctor said. He closed his bag with a snap. "Animal bites. A healthy young woman like your sister here will soon be well again."

"In her body," Edward said quietly. "What about her mind?"

"A holiday will do her good," the doctor suggested. "Get her away from this place. We don't want her to be upset by the local rumours, do we?"

Edward took the doctor by the arm and led him out of the bedroom. When they were in the downstairs hall he said, "What rumours, doctor?"

The man looked embarrassed. "Silly nonsense the Croglin people say."

"About what?"

"These attacks."

"There's been more than one?"

"About ten . . . in the last six months," the unhappy man admitted. "Men and women. He seems to have a thirst for human blood. The villagers say it is someone with a sick mind. Perhaps an escaped criminal. I believe, as I said, it is an animal of some sort."

"Then the sooner we get Amelia away from here the better. Hopefully you'll catch this maniac – or animal – in the meantime," Edward said.

The Cranswell brothers took Amelia to Switzerland.

One evening Michael suggested, "We could always

find a new house. Somewhere else in England – or even go back to Australia."

"I love Croglin Old Hall," she said simply. "I want to go back."

"That creature . . . aren't you afraid?"

"No. If it's still out there then I'll just have to sleep with my shutters closed. I'll move into the West room. I'll be between you and Edward. There are joining doors and I'll leave them unlocked." She gave a relaxed laugh. "If it'll make you happy you can even sleep with a loaded gun beneath your bed."

"Oh, I will," her brother said grimly. "I will."

"Just make sure you shoot the right one . . . I don't want another nightgown ruined with blood!"

"It's not funny," Michael said seriously.

"You're right . . . that nightdress cost me fifteen pounds!" Amelia laughed.

That winter the only things to rattle the Croglin shutters were the gales. Amelia learned to sleep soundly again. She missed the views of the distant mountains from the window of her old room. Now she overlooked the churchyard. She couldn't even see that after sunset, because she was keeping her wooden shutters closed.

As winter melted into spring those shutters began to rattle in the mad March winds. Half awake, Amelia listened to their steady clicking. Click, click, click. The sound began to soothe her to sleep.

Then the clicking stopped. The creaking of hinges and splintering of wood began, slowly at first, then more wildly as something ripped relentlessly at the shutters until they were torn off. This time Amelia found her voice at once. She cried out in terror. The window pane shattered just as Michael rushed into the room. He fired at the shape at the window and heard a scream more hideous than anything he'd heard on this earth.

Leaving his brother to comfort Amelia, Michael hurtled down the stairs, unbolted the back door and was in time to see the sinister shape loping across the lawn. He fired twice. The creature stopped. It fixed the man with its glowing red eyes then limped off down the road to the church.

The young Australian sprinted after it, trying to re-load his revolver as he ran. The shambling, bony thing leapt over the cemetery wall with Michael snatching at its heels. He himself struggled to climb the same wall with the clumsy gun in his hand. At last he reached the top and looked down into the churchyard. The creature bared its fangs at him. Michael aimed the gun and fired.

"It vanished," he said the next morning. "I'd have sworn I hit it three or four times. I'm a good shot! I know it was dark in the graveyard, but I'll swear it was hovering over a huge, flat gravestone one moment and the next it had gone. It could only have slipped below the ground!"

The vicar of the church nodded his long, thin head. "That is an old family grave," he said. "A strange and solitary family. Few people ever saw them in the light of day. The last one died the year before last. I performed the burial service myself."

"Two years ago," Amelia cut in. "Wasn't that around the time the attacks started?"

"Your attacker was no ghost, Miss Cranswell. Ghosts do not cause such injuries to people. And why would a spirit break a window? I have never seen one myself, but I understand such spirits simply walk through walls."

"So we're looking for something that is not dead like a ghost . . . but isn't truly alive either," Edward said.

"The undead," Michael said softly. "I've heard they exist in Europe. Never in England. They live in a grave and come out only at night. They live on fresh blood."

Edward turned pale but Amelia said boldly, "Then it is a menace so long as it stays in our churchyard. No one is safe. We must do something about it."

"Oh, I couldn't possibly let you dig up my graveyard," the vicar muttered miserably.

"Then we shall do it when you are not there, Vicar," the young woman told him.

The vicar cleared his throat. "I will ask my two gravediggers to call on you . . . I shall be going to Carlisle this afternoon," he said. "Remember, I know nothing about your plans." He picked up his hat and hurried out of the door.

"So? What are we waiting for?" Amelia demanded.

"We'll go and gather a few villagers to help too," Edward offered. "We'll tell you what happened when we return."

"That won't be necessary, brother dear," she smiled. "I'll be there to see for myself."

The high walls sheltered the diggers from the chill wind. Fresh spring grass and daffodils were pushing through the soil in the sunlit areas of the graveyard. But around the great grey gravestone where they were working, the plants were as withered as they had been all winter.

It took the men just half an hour to uncover the first of the coffins. They were puzzled to see that they had been broken open. Faded ivory bones were scattered round the crumbling wood.

The last coffin was as strong and solid as ever. Amelia clutched a handkerchief to her nose as they levered off the lid to reveal the withered but undamaged body of the creature who had attacked her. A man once, but now a bloodless figure with a hairless scalp that sent a shiver down her spine. It gave off the same foul odour that she had smelt in her bedroom. It seemed as if the eyes were not quite lifeless. They stared at the diggers as if to hypnotise them.

"Bullet holes!" Amelia said in a hoarse whisper. "You did hit him after all, Michael!"

His sister's voice broke the spell for Michael. "There's only one way to dispose of a monster like this," he said. "Pass me that stake of wood," he ordered.

One of the gravediggers dragged his eyes away from the beast in the coffin and handed a sharpened piece of wood to the young Australian. Michael jumped into the grave, stood astride the creature and raised the stake above his head. He drove it into the skinny chest as hard as he could. A hissing sigh

17

seemed to come from the coffin . . . then silence.

The men lifted the coffin from the grave and took it to the next field where branches trimmed from trees had been drying all winter. They placed the coffin and its owner in the middle of the wood, then set fire to it. After half an hour only smouldering ashes remained. The March wind blew them over the fields.

New life was springing from the ground everywhere. Old death would never rise again.

The Croglin Vampire — Facts

1. The most famous vampire is Count Dracula, the creation in 1897 of the Irish writer Bram Stoker. As a child, Bram Stoker was quite ill. For the first eight years of his life he was confined to bed. During that time his mother told him stories about the plague. Later on these stories inspired him to write his great horror classic. When his book was published it was a sensation throughout Britain. Suddenly tales of strange blood-sucking creatures were being reported everywhere. They were obviously copied from the Bram Stoker character.

2. The remarkable thing about the Croglin Vampire is that its story was first reported in local newspapers in 1875 – that is twenty-two years _before_ Dracula. (The story of Dracula is based upon a real person – Vlad V of Wallachia (1431-76). He was not actually a vampire but a _very_ cruel person. He impaled his enemies on sharp stakes as a warning to anyone thinking of attacking him. One story tells of how he became so angry with a group of visiting ambassadors who forgot to take their turbans off to him, that he had their turbans nailed to their heads.)

3. If you believe in vampires – the undead who rise from their graves each night to suck the blood of living humans – then the story needs no explanation. It is simply a fact.

4. *Such beliefs were common in Eastern Europe in the Middle Ages. The word "vampire" was first used in the English language in 1732. It came from German and French stories of vampire superstitions in the Balkans. (The word nightmare comes from the Anglo-Saxon demon Mara who smothered her victims to death.) The most famous real-life female vampire was Elizabeth Bathroy (1560-1614). She was a Hungarian noblewoman who thought that blood would make her younger. She is supposed to have been responsible for the death of 650 people. She would drink her victims' blood and bathe in it.*

5. *Another theory about vampires is that they are people infected by rabid dogs. Victims of rabies have been known to act like animals and even bite people.*

6. *If you think you have found a vampire, garlic, crucifixes, mustard and poppy seeds, tar and holy water are supposed to protect you. But do not leave home without stakes, a mallet, rope, a flashlight, a mirror and crowbar.*

7. *If you don't believe in living corpses, then you need to decide what really happened at Croglin. Look at the story step by step and take out what is possible, what is imagined and what is invented:*

Possible: Someone broke into Amelia's bedroom and attacked her. After she had screamed he ran away the way he had come in. That "someone" was the demented person villagers had reported earlier. When the second attack occurred, Michael Cranswell shot the attacker who limped off to die in some hidden den and was never found. The villagers dug up the grave of an unpopular person. The coffins around had been damaged and the bones scattered when the new coffin had been buried two years before. The body was quite well preserved because it was inside a sealed casket. The superstitious villagers may well have disposed of the body as if it were a vampire.

Imagined: Amelia's "remembered" details of the attacker came from her terror and not her senses. The smell could have been real enough – but the glowing red eyes were probably added by her fear-struck mind. Similarly, the high excitement Michael felt in the chase caused him to be confused by shadows in the graveyard. While the attacker limped off somewhere to die, Michael expected to see him in the graveyard. Humans in an excited or nervous state very often see what they expect to see and not what is really there. After he had fired into the graveyard his eyes cleared and the vision disappeared. How could he explain a vanishing man to himself? He must have vanished under the grave, he thought. And, consequently, as that's what he believed, that's what he reported.

Invented: As stories are repeated over the years the story-tellers add details of their own to make them more dramatic. Finding bullet holes in the body is a neat piece of "proof" of the idea that the attacker and the corpse in the grave were the same man.

2. Jack-o-Lantern

How did telling spooky stories start? Probably when people saw, or heard something they didn't understand, they told stories to explain the strange sights and sounds. These stories would be re-told until they became legends. But some strange sights, like a luminous shape that drifted across the surface of the earth, may well have started off as true sightings. Could a legend like Jack O'Lantern be based on fact?

County Clare, Ireland – A Long Time Ago

Now Jack was probably the wickedest man in the whole of County Clare. Maybe the wickedest man in Ireland. He was fond of drinking but not so fond of spending his money. He let his poor wife and children work, then took their money and spent it down at the local inn.

But one night Jack went a little too far. As he wandered home from the inn, he stumbled into a ditch at the side of the road and couldn't be bothered to climb out again. As his body lay there, his spirit began to slip out of it.

"Got you!" the Devil cried and grabbed Jack's soul by the hair.

Jack woke up and struggled to hang on to his soul.

"Hey! Let go!" he cried.

"I won't," the Devil laughed. "I've waited years for your wicked soul and now it's all mine."

Jack was not quite ready to let his soul go down to Hell. He was a clever man for all he was lazy, mean and cruel. "Now Devil," he sighed, "I think you're right. I'll have to go with you some time so it might as well be this night. But I've heard Hell is a terrible hot place. I'd have liked just one last drink before you roast me on your iron bars."

"Iron bars!" the Devil cried. "You foolish man, you know the Devil and all his kind cannot abide the touch of iron."

"Is that so, now?" Jack asked and rubbed a hand across the ginger stubble on his chin. "But what about that drink? You must be wanting one yourself, and Leary's beer's the best in all of County Clare. Perhaps the best in all of Ireland."

The Devil ran a purple tongue across his dark, dry lips. "You could be right," he sighed. "A drink before we go to Hell would be very nice."

And so the two set off along the road. Then, as they reached the corner of the street, that crafty Jack let out a long low groan.

"What's wrong?" the Devil asked. "Don't tell me that Leary's bar is closed."

"I've just remembered. When I left the bar I had just sixpence in my purse. Enough to buy myself a drink but not enough for you. I'll have to ask you if you'll pay for your own beer, my friend."

The Devil danced a little jig of anger on the dusty street. "Now Jack, don't you know, the Devil never carries cash."

"Sure that's a shame," the man said and he shook his head. "No doubt you change yourself into a coin whenever you go drinking."

"I do?" the Devil said, astonished by and then liking the thought. "Of course I do."

"So change yourself to sixpence and just hop inside this purse," the crafty Jack said.

Then the Devil closed his eyes and slowly turned as silver as the moon. Then he shrank and started to turn round and small. In just a half-a-minute he was tucked up snug inside the purse of crafty Jack.

"Oh, Devil!" Jack cried softly to the purse. "Perhaps you didn't notice, but this purse is fastened with an iron cross. I know you don't like iron and I know you can't stand crosses. Tell me, Devil, how will you get out of my old purse?"

"You'll let me out!" the Devil's tiny voice squeaked.

"Oh, no I won't," the man replied. "What? Let you out to steal away my soul. I may be mean – and some say that I'm wicked – but no one ever says I'm daft as that. You're in my purse and there you'll stay."

"You let me out!" the Devil raged. "You'll never have a moment's peace as long as I am trapped in here."

The man sighed, "That's the truth. I'll tell you what. I'll let you out, but you must swear to go away and leave my soul alone."

"I can't do that. Your soul is mine. Your wicked ways made sure of that. Some day I'll have to take you down to Hell."

"I'll tell you what," the man said softly. "Go away and leave me for one year – twelve months – and then come back again."

"Agreed!" the Devil cried.

Jack let him out. The Devil swelled back to his ugly shape and breathed his stinking breath into the cruel man's face. "A year from now is Hallowe'en. I'll be back then. I'll make you pay for that trick, Jack. You see if I don't make you pay!" he roared and vanished down into the ground.

"Not if I mend my ways," the man said and he walked home slowly, thinking hard.

Next morning Jack's wife almost fell out of her bed. Her husband stood there at the bedside with a cup of tea.

"What's this?"

"For you my darling. You lie there. Today I'll go out in the fields and do the weeding, feed the sheep." Then he put the tea down, found his work boots and set off to work.

"What's wrong with dad?" his children asked. Jack's wife just sat and shook her head. "I think the Devil's turned his brain to water."

Jack worked hard and Jack worked long. He even took himself to church. But the Devil smiled and the Devil waited and, sure enough, Jack turned back to his old ways.

Next Hallowe'en night he was hurrying back from the inn when he saw the Devil waiting for him by Farmer Rooney's orchard. "Good evening, Jack. It's time for you to come with me. I've got a seat all ready for you by the fire."

"That's kind of you," Jack said. "There's nothing I like better than a roasted apple. Roasted by your fires they'd taste just fine."

The Devil looked at Jack. Was this another of his crafty tricks? "An apple did you say?" and licked his lips.

"The ones from off the very top of Farmer Rooney's tree taste better than all other apples in the whole of County Clare – or in the whole of Ireland come to that."

"And how am I supposed to reach the top?" the Devil asked.

"Here, climb up on my shoulders," Jack replied and helped the Devil up into the tree. The Devil's feet were like a goat's and the hooves dug deep into his neck. "Just hang on to the tree," Jack moaned. "Take the weight off just a moment."

The devil stretched his arms and swung up on a branch. Jack rubbed his shoulders. Then he walked towards the trunk, quickly took a knife from out of his coat pocket and carved a cross into the bark . . . The Devil screamed. "I can't get down! You know I can't get down from a tree that's had a cross carved on it!"

Jack just smiled and said, "Now, swear to let me live in peace for ever more. If you do, I'll cut that branch from off the tree."

"Agreed!" the Devil cried.

Sly Jack lopped off the branch and laughed to see the Devil fall and let the ground just swallow him.

"That's that!" said he, dusting off his hands. "I'll live in peace."

But crafty Jack was wrong. Long before next Hallowe'en his evil living brought about his death. The family buried him in a dark corner of the village churchyard and then went back home to celebrate.

"Now, there's a thing!" Jack's soul said. "What do I do now? I suppose I get myself on up to Heaven."

But when he reached Heaven's gate, Saint Peter said, "You can't come in. A wicked man like you belongs in Hell."

"A wicked man!" Jack said. "Who said that I'm a wicked man? Just name me one!"

"More to the point, there's not one who will speak up for you. You can't come in, so go to Hell."

The soul of Jack just shrugged its ghostly shoulders and went off to find the door to Hell.

"I'm Jack," he told the little devil standing at the entrance. "Tell my old friend that I'm here."

The devil closed the door in Jack's ghost face and hurried inside with the message. In a moment he returned. "The Devil says he doesn't want you. You're more trouble than you're worth."

Jack tried to push his way inside but the Devil saw him, gave a roar and threw a piece of hell-fire at him. Jack caught the fire, just before the little devil slammed the door hard shut. He took the fire and popped it in a carved-out turnip.

From that day on Jack's wandered round the earth,

his turnip lantern swinging in the midnight breezes.
And still he plays his wicked tricks.

Jack-o-Lantern — Facts

1. Jack o'Lantern is obviously a legend. But where do such stories come from? Why do people tell them? Lights and ghosts go together. Some of the strangest ghostly appearances are of lights that appear in lonely places and drift around. They are often thought to be a bad sign – a sign that there will shortly be a death in that place. They are also seen as evil, because travellers may follow the light and not the road. They are led into danger or end up lost. It would seem that such lights are reported too often for them to be ignored.

2. Roman historians recorded mystery lights as long ago as 216 BC. The writer Julius Obsequens recorded, "Things like ships were seen in the sky above Italy – at Arpi a round shield was seen in the sky and at Capua the sky was all on fire." Five hundred years later, a medieval historian, Conrad Wolffhart, wrote, "Strange lights were seen in the sky in the days of the Roman Emperor Theodosius. All of a sudden a bright globe appeared in the sky at midnight. It shone brilliantly near the planet Venus. By and by a great number of other glowing orbs drew near the first globe and swarmed around it like bees around a bee-keeper." These reports of strange lights in ancient Rome have been explained by modern investigators . . . as proof that there were flying saucers in ancient times!

3. *Halley's Comet, which appears every 76 years or so, has been taken as a mysterious sign in the sky. It was seen in 1066, before the Battle of Hastings, and taken as a sign of doom for King Harold. Of course, it could also have been a sign of good luck for William the Conqueror who won the battle!*

4. *In Brazil seeing a drifting light called the "Mother of Gold" is definitely lucky. The glowing orange-yellow ball, about the size of a human head, moves slowly. If you can follow it, and look in the first river or lake that it crosses, then you will find a fortune in gold. Local people say that the area in which it has been reported (from 1830 to 1980) is haunted.*

5. *Scientists explain that strange lights are seen in the sky when disturbances in the atmosphere "bend" the light from natural sources like the sun, the moon and the stars.*

6. *Lights nearer the ground are often caused by a gas from the earth known as "marsh gas" or methane. On the Mitchell Flats in Texas they are known as Marfa lights. The Native American Indians explained them as the soul of a brave, wandering the earth looking for his lost love. Texas legends say they are the ghost of a ranch owner who returns every year on his birthday – or the ghostly lights of the campfire from an old wagon train that was wiped out in an attack. During World War II the lights were mistaken for signals from secret agents*

guiding enemy paratroopers into the country. As with the Roman lights, some investigators say they are Unidentified Flying Objects (UFOs).

7. *Mystery lights like these have been seen all around the world and given different names including Will-o'-the-wisp, corpse candles, dead candles, spook-lights, Jenny-burnt-tail or Kit-in-the-candlestick. The Irish call them Jack-o'-Lanterns.*

7. *If you see a light while you're out wandering after dark, what should you do? Just turn your jacket inside out to let Jack see you have no money for his greedy hands. Then he should leave you all alone and go off to bother someone else. Or would you like to study the light the way a scientist records an experiment? That's what one group was set up to do. A number of people interested in spirits formed the Society for Psychical Research in 1882. They have published many reports including* Phantasms of the Living *in 1886. This included a "guide" for anyone who thinks they have seen something supernatural.*

3. The House in Portman Square

*Stories of a haunted house are quite common.
Someone living there sees a phantom figure – the
ghost of someone who lived and died there in the past.
Most of these ghosts have tragic histories but they do
no harm to the living. The ghosts of Portman Square,
on the other hand, had a terrible and frightening way
of dealing with anyone trying to share their home . . .*

Portman Square, London – 1911

It was a strange and rambling house, full of old oak
stairways. Long and narrow corridors seemed to hold
dark and evil secrets. Windows gave no warming
sunlight, only gloomy views of shadowed courtyards
at the back and the blank, blind faces of houses at the
front.

After sunset a shroud of darkness seemed to wrap
itself around the house before creeping slowly inside.
Blazing log fires hardly seemed to warm the rooms

and hissing gaslight was strangely dimmed.

But the house was cheap.

"Why so cheap?" the doctor asked the agent who was renting it.

The man spread his hands. "I could tell you all sorts of tales, doctor. But you are a sensible man. I will tell you the truth. The house has a bad name."

"A name for what?" the doctor grunted.

"Er . . . for being haunted," the agent replied.

"Stuff and nonsense. I don't believe that sort of claptrap. What is it? Some pale-faced woman in a black dress drifting along the corridors when midnight strikes?"

"No. Nothing like that," the agent said. "It concerns a lady who lived here in the days of the old queen . . ."

"Which old queen? Boadicea? Elizabeth the first?"

"Victoria, Sir."

"If you mean Victoria why don't you say Victoria?" the doctor snapped as he marched down the dim corridors and tried each room in turn. The worn carpets added to the sad and neglected look of the place. Dust lay thick on the few sticks of furniture left in the rooms.

"Sorry, sir," the agent said in a softly whining voice. He rubbed his hands together as if he were washing them. "The old queen . . . it's a figure of speech."

"I am happier with plain speech. Get on with your story."

"Of course, sir. The lady who lived here, a Mrs Strawn, was lying in bed one night when she heard a clock striking in the hallway. The clock struck thirteen."

"Amazing," the doctor snorted. "She called in a clockmaker to repair it, did she?"

"Ah, that was the problem," the agent said. "You see, there was no clock in the hallway."

"Bit difficult to repair it then," the doctor said with a short, barking laugh.

"Precisely, sir. But after the clock had struck thirteen, she heard it strike again slowly, five times. To her horror her husband died . . . five days later!"

"Was he ill at the time?" the doctor asked suspiciously.

"Oh, no, doctor. He died in an accident while roller skating at a London rink."

"Serves him right," the doctor muttered and began to climb the narrow stairway to the upstairs rooms.

The agent hurried after him and panted, "This is where Mrs Strawn heard the clock."

"The clock that wasn't there?"

"Exactly, sir."

"She was probably shocked at the man's death and came up with the story afterwards. It's called hysteria, you know."

"If you say so, sir. But the lady did try to have the house exorcised by a priest."

"More poppycock!" the doctor sniffed.

"Then, two years later, Mrs Strawn heard the clock strike thirteen again . . . and this time it was followed by three slow chimes."

"So, the priest couldn't fix a clock either, eh?" the doctor mumbled.

"The lady knew that her aunt was sick," the agent went on. "After the clock struck thirteen and three, the lady expected to hear of her death in three days time."

"And would you believe it!" the doctor cried. "Lo and behold, the aunt died three days later. Am I right? Pah! If the woman was sick then it was easy to guess that she would die in around three days. Lucky guess."

The agent stopped at the door to a bedroom. He seemed unwilling to go in. "No, sir. Mrs Strawn went out into Portman Square in a cab. It was involved in a crash. A window shattered and a piece of glass stabbed her throat. It was as if the clock had been predicting her death . . . a woman who hoped to live another twenty or thirty years! . . . not her sickly aunt's death! How do you explain that, sir?"

The doctor didn't answer. "This is the room, is it?" he asked suddenly.

"Yes, doctor. But you can sleep in one of the others of course." This one had a musty smell as if it hadn't been used for years. There was an iron bedstead in the middle of the floor. The wallpaper had once been pale green. Now it was fading to a yellowy brown. The window looked out onto a back yard. Spring sunlight warmed the walls of the houses opposite. The sun had never shone in this room.

"Do I look like the sort of man who would be put off by a few fairy stories?" the doctor asked.

"Oh, no, sir. Certainly not sir!"

"Then I'll take the house . . . and I'll sleep here."

The agent turned a little pale but nodded and said, "As you wish, sir."

The agent didn't visit the house for another three months. When he did he was shocked by what he saw. The doctor's face was pale and lined. Dark circles surrounded his eyes and his hair seemed to have turned grey in such a short time.

The agent forgot to ask for the rent. Instead he stepped into the gaslit hall and said, "How are you keeping doctor? If you will excuse my saying so, you don't look too well."

"I have lost some weight," the doctor admitted.

"The house is comfortable, is it sir?" the agent asked.

"The house is a doorway to hell," the doctor said in a flat voice. "Oh, don't worry. I haven't gone mad. I know you warned me about sleeping in that room. I know I jeered at your superstition. You will not find me jeering now."

"I'm sorry," the agent said sincerely. "Perhaps I can arrange for you to have a new house . . ."

"That is no use," the doctor sighed and led the way into the living room. "I'm afraid I am doomed. Take a seat by the fire and I'll tell you about it."

The men sat facing each other. The doctor stirred at the coal with a poker and began talking in a low, spiritless voice. "The first week was fine. I slept well, though the room felt unusually cold. Nothing I could do seemed to warm it. I realise now the coldness was my first warning. I ignored it so I had to be given a much more serious warning. The warning came in the form of a dream. Perhaps I should say a nightmare. For I dreamed that a man appeared at the door of the room. His face was as pale as a corpse and he was dressed in a fine black suit. He beckoned me with his hand. I knew I was meant to follow him."

The doctor shuddered as he remembered the apparition. "He only said one word. 'Come.' I didn't want to follow him but I felt I had to. I rose from my bed and followed him through the door. Then he led me down the stairs. Not just into the hallway here but further down into the cellar. And from the cellar he led me down still further into the earth. So many steps. I thought we'd never stop, but at last we reached an underground room. I didn't want to enter. My guide said, 'Come!' again and again I had to follow him. There was a table in the room."

The doctor uncorked a bottle of sherry and poured out two glasses. His hand was trembling. "There was a group of people seated around the table. Men and women. Each had a face as white as my guide. Each face held an expression of terror. Then the man sitting at the end of the table turned towards me. His face was the most hideously ugly thing I have ever seen . . . half human and half animal. He pointed to a chair. He wanted me to sit there. I wanted to refuse but I couldn't."

The doctor threw back the sherry in one swallow and stared into the flickering flame of the fire. "Suddenly I found the courage to escape. I jumped to my feet and ran for the door. One of the women grabbed my sleeve. I tried to tear free but she had the strength of ten horses. She laughed as I struggled. 'It's no use,' she cried. 'You can't get away. We are all of us trapped here until the end of time and longer.' I shouted at her, 'Why? What have I done to deserve this? I'm innocent of any crime.' The animal man sniggered at me and spoke in a voice as hollow as a coffin. 'Your crime is that you slept in that room. Every one of us has slept in that room and had to come here in the end.' The rest of the white-faced group nodded and groaned in agreement."

The doctor rose from the fireside and pushed his forehead against the cool marble mantelpiece to clear his fevered head. "The man introduced me to each one in turn. The oldest, thinnest man was called Robert Percival. A young woman was called Sarah Hackett. An older woman was Mrs Emma Freeman. The tall man with a beard was Colonel William Sacherell. The old couple were Mr and Mrs Strawn."

"The ones I told you about?" the agent cut in.

The doctor nodded. "It seems the fate of everyone who sleeps in that bedroom is doomed to end in the cellar with that ghoulish group. The ugly man explained to me, 'Everyone who sleeps there is drawn by our power sooner or later.' Then he said the most gruesome thing I have ever heard. He said that I was free to go . . . but I must promise to return to them on 21 June."

The doctor took a deep breath. "Of course I was so desperate to escape from those demons that I said, 'Yes – I promise.' No sooner had I said it than the room vanished. I woke in my own bed."

The agent rubbed his hands with that hand-washing action of his. "A very bad dream," he said. "I'm sorry I frightened you with my silly ghost story about the Strawns."

"You didn't frighten me," the doctor sighed. "You

told me about the Strawns – you didn't tell me about the others. I have never heard their names until I saw them in that vision."

"You invented the names in your dream . . ." the agent began.

"No. I went to the town hall and checked on the lists of residents. Every one of those names was real. They did live here." His eyes opened wide as he turned to the agent. "How do you explain that?"

"Not to worry, sir. Take a holiday. Don't go back on 21 June . . ."

"I promised!" the doctor groaned. "If I don't go back then the fiends will find a way of making me."

"Now, now, sir. That's just your imagination. How could spirits of the dead make a living man do something against his will?"

"You'll see," the doctor said and his voice was hoarse.

"I'll tell you what, Sir. I'll call back next week on 21 June. Once you've put that day behind you then you'll see how you are no more than a victim of your own fears. This house is a little gloomy for a lonely man." He rose from the chair and crossed to the door. "I'll see myself out, sir. I look forward to seeing you again on 21 June. You will be all right, sir. You'll see."

He let himself out of the front door and hurried down the street. It wasn't until he reached his office that he realised he had not collected the rent.

There was no answer when he knocked on the door, but the agents always kept copies of the keys. He let himself into the dark hallway. "Doctor?" he called. A mouse scuttled away from him. There was no other sound.

He tapped on the living room door and opened it. The ashes were cold in the grate. Then he climbed the stairs warily. There was no need to search the upper floor. He went straight to the bedroom and tapped on the door. When there was no reply, he pushed the door open. The doctor was lying on the bed. His face had an expression of sadness and fear. He was dead.

The police surgeon declared that the dead man had suffered a heart attack. "Just after midnight, I'd say. That's today. So what date is it?" he asked.

"The twenty-first of June," the agent said quietly.

The House in Portman Square — Facts

1. This story never reached the newspapers because it was the tale of nothing more than a man dying from a heart attack. But the doctor's nephew knew the full facts and repeated them to a psychic researcher ten years later.

2. One sensible explanation is that the doctor was more afraid of the old ghost story than he liked to admit. He slept in the haunted room to prove how brave he was. In fact he was so scared that he had nightmares. The people in the room below the cellar were just part of a dream. Nevertheless that nightmare frightened the doctor. He was sure he would die on 21 June. When that day arrived the strain was too much for his heart. He frightened himself to death.

3. Can a spirit predict when a person is going to die? Giving the actual date of death is rare. But there are many cases of a spirit appearing and the witness dying shortly afterwards. In Ireland such spirits are called banshees. A banshee is usually a woman and she is attached to a family. When this crying woman is seen, it is said to be a sign that someone in that family will die shortly.

4. Can you dream of your own death? The American President Abraham Lincoln did. He told of a dream in which he rose from his bed and walked down the

stairs of the White House. He then entered a room containing many crying people gathered around a coffin. When he went into the room he looked into the coffin and saw the body was his own! Within a year President Lincoln was assassinated by a gunman. Several people have since claimed to see Lincoln's ghost in the White House.

5. Can you make a date with a ghost? Making a date with a ghost and agreeing to visit it on the day of your death is thankfully not common. But there are many recorded cases of living people arranging with a living friend to visit them after they die . . . and keeping the appointment. One of the most famous cases of this nature concerns Lord Henry Brougham (1778 – 1868), who was at college with his great friend Geoffrey Garner. Over the years they drifted apart and saw little of each other until Brougham went on a visit to Sweden. This is his own story . . .

"Arriving at a decent inn, we decided to stop for the night. I was glad to take advantage of a hot bath before I turned in, and here a most remarkable thing happened to me – so remarkable that I must tell the story from the beginning.

After I left High School, I went with Garner, my closest friend, to classes at university. We often discussed many serious subjects, among others, what happened to the soul after death and the after life. This question, and the possibility of the dead appearing to the living, were the subjects of much discussion. We actually committed the folly of

43

drawing up an agreement, written in our blood. We agreed that whichever of us died first should appear to the other and solve any doubts we had about life after death.

After we had finished university Garner went to India. He seldom wrote to me and, after a few years, I had almost forgotten him. His family had no connection with Edinburgh where I lived and where we went to university so I seldom saw or heard anything of him and had nearly forgotten his existence.

I had taken a warm bath. I was lying in it and enjoying the comfort of the heat after the freezing I had suffered. I turned my head around, looking towards the chair on which I had deposited my clothes, as I was about to get out of the bath. On the chair sat Garner, looking calmly at me.

How I got out of the bath I really do not know. On recovering my senses I found myself sprawling on the floor. The spirit, or whatever it was that had taken the appearance of Garner, had disappeared."

When Lord Brougham returned to Edinburgh he heard that Garner had died in India on 19 December . . . the very day that he had appeared in Brougham's bathroom. Curiously enough, Lord Brougham used to say he did not believe in ghosts, even after his meeting with the dead Garner. He said he had probably just imagined Garner's appearance and that the date of his death was just a coincidence.

4. The Ghost Hunter

*Many people have tried to hunt for ghosts. They hope
that they can prove that ghosts exist. A photograph of
a ghost may make them rich. It could make them
famous! It could also make them cheat! Which ghost
hunter could you believe? Someone who is simply
seeking the truth? Someone who has nothing to gain
from telling lies? Someone like a medieval monk . . .*

Alais, Southern France – 1323
This letter is addressed to Abbot Wilfred of the
Benedictine Monastery of Paris from Brother John
Goby of the Benedictine Monastery of Avignon.

My dear friend and brother, I have received your
letter. Many thanks for your good wishes – and your
curiosity!

So you've heard the strange story already, have
you? I am writing a report for His Holiness The Pope,

but it will do no harm to tell you my tale. I know it will be safe with you.

This strange and unhappy story began a month ago. In late November a merchant died in the town of Alais, just forty miles north of here.

The merchant's name was Guy de Torno. He was buried in the town churchyard and should have lain in peace. But shortly after his burial, travelling friars began arriving at the Pope's palace here in Avignon with reports that the merchant's ghost was haunting his widow. His voice had been troubling the widow's sleep each night.

Those are the simple facts of the case. The rumours reached His Holiness just before Christmas.

As we know, a ghost is a tragic spirit. One who is too sinful to enter heaven – but not evil enough to enter hell. It is in a state of Purgatory. Once it has suffered enough it will be allowed into Heaven. The Pope was worried about the effect the spirit was having on the innocent widow. He called me to him.

"Brother John," he said. "You have some success in exorcising spirits, have you not?"

"I have driven evil spirits out of houses and out of people," I admitted.

"I would like you to go to the town of Alais and look into the haunting of a widow there," he said.

"I have heard the stories," I said.

"And what do you think of them?"

I chose my words carefully. "The matters I have looked into before have been clear cases of the Devil at work. This is different. It is supposed to be the spirit of a Christian man who cannot rest. I cannot simply drive him to Hell the way I do with devils."

Now, Wilfred, as you know, the Pope has a sharp mind and he leaned forward and asked me alertly, "What do you mean when you say 'supposed to be'?"

Again I was slow to answer. "I mean that we must first look at the possibility of human trickery," I told him.

"Good, Brother John. Good. That is what I thought when I heard the widow's tale. I would like you to go to Alais. Do not perform any services to exorcise the devil. Just look very carefully at the woman's story. Imagine the damage she could do to our church!" he said.

I knew exactly what he meant. This woman could be performing some conjuring trick. If we were fooled by her, then the whole church would look foolish. Wouldn't the Devil love that? I decided that the first thing I must do at Alais was to look for trickery to make quite sure that this was indeed the spirit of the dead merchant. If it was a spirit from Purgatory, then it could be dealt with.

Pope John XXII said nothing else but his look said, "Study this case . . . but don't be too quick to believe in ghosts!"

We sent messages ahead to Alais Monastery to tell them we would be arriving. Two days later we set off.

I know you said you have had snow in Paris, but it is rare down here in the south. Still we do have the Mistral winds. We had to head straight into their biting coldness. The horses put their heads down and plodded slowly northwards. After a day my feet were numb in my boots, my hands frozen to the reins. The only shelter was in the forests . . . and there we feared attacks from the robber bands who lie in wait like wild animals.

Perhaps it was too cold for them to leave their fires. Perhaps they respected our monks' habits. Perhaps the Lord protected us. Whatever, we reached Alais frozen but uninjured two days later. The monastery offered us shelter. We said prayers of thanks for our safe arrival. Then I began the task the Pope had set me.

I didn't visit the widow at once. I wanted to know as much as possible about the dead man and his life before I called on her.

The mayor of the town and some of his oldest councillors joined me for supper. I'm sure you know the sort of men. Dressed in furs and silks. They would sell their souls for a purse of gold. You cannot trust such men. I knew they were lying when they were asked about Guy de Torno.

"A fine man," a clerk said in a whining voice.

"One of the best," the mayor agreed.

"Then what sin could prevent him from entering Heaven?" I asked.

"He was a fine man," the clerk repeated helplessly.

"Was it greed?" I asked. "Was he too fond of fine clothes, perhaps?"

The councillors tugged at their fur trimming and were too ashamed to answer. I had a feeling they knew about de Torno's sins but were protecting the man's memory. Maybe they shared his sin, who knows? "I will need your help," I said coldly, but with all the authority of the Pope behind me.

"Anything, sir . . . I mean Abbot John," the mayor

said eagerly.

"The people of Alais trust you," I said. I was tempted to add, "The good Lord knows why."

The men looked pleased. Clearly pride was another of their sins.

"They trust you, so they will be reassured if you witness my investigation. Wherever I go I want a respectable citizen of Alais to go with me. Are there a hundred honest people in Alais?" I asked. Was there just one?, I wondered. "Can you find them for me and bring them to Guy de Torno's house tomorrow morning?"

They said they could. True to their word, the witnesses assembled at the fine house of the dead merchant the next day. "First I will search the garden," I announced. "I want some of you to come with me. I want the rest to form a circle outside the wall. No one must be allowed to enter."

Now, Wilfred, I will be honest, I do not know what I was looking for. Something – anything – unusual or out of place. I found nothing.

I then called on the widow. I took with me two of my brothers from Avignon, two brothers from Alais and a respectable elderly woman.

"Good morning, Madame de Torno. I am Brother John, sent by the Pope to investigate this visitation from your husband." The woman had a hard and bitter face. Her mouth was thin and drawn down at the corners. She wore black, as a widow should.

"Come in," she said, her voice sour as vinegar.

"Where do these visitations take place?" I asked.

"Everywhere in this sad house," she said, "but

mainly in the bedroom."

"Then shall we begin there?" She led the way up the stairs to the bedroom. A dim room with cupboards, a dressing table and, as you would expect, a bed. It was a huge piece of furniture with heavy curtains to keep the Mistral out. My brothers and I checked every corner and panel of the room. There seemed to be no secret doorways, passages or rooms where a cunning helper could hide. If a ghost appeared now, it would have to be a true, troubled spirit.

"Lie upon the bed, Madame," I ordered. The elderly woman from Alais was asked to lie beside her to check for trickery. A brother sat at each corner. "We will now perform a ceremony called the Office of the Dead. It will protect you from demons."

The woman nodded silently, lay back and stared at the canopy over the bed.

We began the ceremony. The brothers had only chanted two lines when we were disturbed. There was the sound of scratching from above the bed. Imagine a brush being dragged across the floor of the room above, Wilfred, and you will know what I mean.

I hurried to the window. There was nothing outside. I went to the door. The Mistral was howling outside but that was not the sound we heard. I crossed to the door. A dozen or so of the people from Alais waited there. "Search the room above – quickly!" I whispered and went back to the side of the bed. "Was that your husband?" I asked.

The woman didn't reply. Instead a faint voice answered, "Yes it is me . . . Guy de Torno."

Before I could question him the door flew open. The brothers believed it was the dead man's spirit! They jumped to their feet in confusion and grabbed at the crosses around their necks. In fact is was some of the Alais witnesses. They had been listening at the door and were overcome with curiosity.

Imagine my annoyance, Wilfred! Yes, I know, anger is a deadly sin . . . and I confess I came close to it then. You know how loud my voice can be when I am singing in church, don't you? I used its full force to clear the room. It frightened the witnesses . . . I wondered if I had also frightened away the spirit of Guy de Torno himself.

My brothers faced the bed and one at a time they began to question the voice. From the shadows of the curtained bed the answers came in that same thin, distant voice. I took notes. I make a copy of them for you here, Wilfred.

Monk: Are you the spirit of Guy de Torno?
Spirit: I am.
Monk: Are you from the devil?
Spirit: I am not.
Monk: Where are you from?
Spirit: I am in limbo. The world between this world and the next.
Monk: Why are you there?
Spirit: For my sins on earth.
Monk: What sins were they?
Spirit: I was not faithful to my wife.
Monk: Why do you haunt her?
Spirit: I am seeking her forgiveness.
Monk: And if she gives it to you?

Spirit: Then I hope I will be allowed into Heaven.

So, Guy de Torno had been unfaithful to his wife. I had no doubt that the mayor and his rich friends knew that. This was the secret they hoped to keep from me when I asked about the merchant's sins. These town people have a foolish superstition – they believe that it's wrong to repeat bad stories about the dead.

I was almost angry again, I can tell you, Wilfred. But any such feelings vanished when the ghost said something quite remarkable. "The abbot has a holy box underneath his robe. That box is so blessed that it has the power to free me from this world!"

The brothers looked towards me. I knew that I had brought with me a holy box. It held a fragment of bone from St Michael himself. Pope John had given it to me secretly before we left Avignon. I would swear that none of the brothers knew about the box. So, tell me, Wilfred. How did the voice know? Unless, of course, that voice was truly a spirit from limbo. Such spirits can move among the living but are invisible to our eyes!

We left quickly after that. It was not my duty to exorcise this spirit. The local priests could try that. It was simply my job to report to the Pope. After one more night at the monastery we rode back to Avignon with the Mistral at our backs.

I have shared my first thoughts with the Pope. He questioned me thoroughly about the investigation and has praised my work. Now I must write a report of the visit for His Holiness.

This letter to you, Wilfred, has helped me to clear my thoughts before I turn back to writing that report.

You may remember I began by saying I went to Alais with an open mind. I looked for trickery and I found none. I did not expect to speak with the spirit of a dead man – now I believe I did.

Truly the Lord works in strange and mysterious ways.

May he protect and keep you until we meet again.

Your devoted brother, John Goby.

The Ghost Hunter — Facts

1. John's report was published in the records of the Catholic Church and is one of the first cases of a true inquiry into a spirit appearance.

2. Religious investigators before John had studied such cases, but had always started by believing that the spirit existed. John's study was the first recorded where the ghost hunter began in the belief that the spirit did not exist.

3. Abbot John was unusual. At that time many Church men did believe in devils and they had a harsh way of dealing with them – the person who was "possessed" by the demon would be burned at the stake. The widow was taking a great risk in claiming to be haunted by her husband's voice. She could well have been tortured and executed. So, knowing the risk, would she deliberately fake it?

4. Either the voice was a ghost or it was a fraud. Which would you believe? Look at the possibilities . . .

The spirit of Guy de Torno was genuine.

- The voice was that of a ghost whose sinful life stopped him from entering the afterlife.
- The voice was that of a spirit rather like a poltergeist – this is a powerful force that is able to throw objects around. The force is said to come from

the mind of a disturbed person.
- *The spirit knew that the holy box was under John's robe – something that no living person knew about. This would seem to prove that the spirit was genuine.*
- *The old woman was lying next to the widow on the bed. She would have been able to tell if the widow was creating the voice, even if the monks outside the bed couldn't.*
- *Abbot John was an intelligent and cautious man. He could not be fooled by tricks or fakes. The spirit had to be genuine.*

The spirit of Guy de Torno was a fraud.
- *Widow de Torno knew that her husband had been seeing another woman. This was a serious offence in the eyes of the Church in the Middle Ages. She had no proof of her suspicions until he had died. She plotted her revenge.*
- *She could have told the people of Alais about her husband's wickedness. They would have smiled and forgotten about it. She wanted the world to know. She wanted something dramatic and unforgettable.*
- *Widow de Torno said she had heard her husband's voice. She knew this would cause the Church to investigate. Once they had investigated, everyone would know about her husband's wrong-doings.*
- *When Abbot John arrived she arranged for a maid to make the brushing sounds in the room above. She then created the spirit voice like a ventriloquist. In the shadows of the bed curtains no one would see her lips move.*
- *Abbot John did a good job but he did finish rather*

suddenly. He didn't question servants about the spirit happenings or about Guy de Torno when was alive. He did not try to speak to the spirit voice a second time – perhaps with the widow in full view of the investigators. Brother John was a clever ghost hunter – Widow de Torno was simply cleverer.

5. The Family Witch

Most ghosts haunt one particular place and return there occasionally – sometimes at the same time each year. If they are seen by humans, then they don't seem to know they are being watched. But there are stories of spooks which seek out humans, torment them and drive them to their death. One famous American ghost is known as the "Bell Witch"...

Tennessee, USA – 1817
So you want to hear about the Bell Witch, do you? I'm the best person to tell you. When I was a girl I was Betsy Bell. I lived through the haunting of our family seventy years ago. That's right. I'm eighty-three now and the trouble all started when I was just twelve years old.

Now, don't ask me why the Witch decided to spook the Bell family but it did. We were no different to a thousand other Tennessee families. Pa owned a farm in Robertson County. Ma and us eight kids were normal, church-going, God-fearing folk.

Like I say, I was twelve when the noises started. When night fell we began to hear strange scratchings. "Rats," Pa said. And they sure sounded like something chewing at the bedposts. We had a dozen house cats and they never let rats within half a mile of the house. The trouble was that when we lit a lantern there were no rats there . . . but the chewing sounds still went on!

Then Pa started seeing a weird animal wandering round the farm. He reckoned it might have been some kind of wild dog. He didn't want it stealing the chickens, so he took his gun out one day and shot it. He swore he couldn't miss, but that dog just stared at him with eyes like burning coals and walked away.

Same thing happened with a large bird. And the shooting just made the old spook angry. The noises grew louder. Nobody could sleep for them. It started tearing covers off the beds and slapping and pinching us.

It seemed to have a specially nasty grudge against me. My hair was pulled, my face slapped. It pinched me and stuck pins in me till I bled.

Of course, we tried to keep it secret, but word got out in the end. Pa was suffering. Said his tongue was beginning to swell in his mouth. He couldn't talk and he couldn't eat. Ma finally called on neighbour James Johnson for help. Neighbour Johnson was a preacher on Sundays and he knew all the right words to drive that spook away. He called in neighbours to help with the praying.

Now, you understand, in our church we didn't

believe in ghosts. James Johnson said it must be a "Witch". That's what folk round about us called it. The "Bell Witch". The name stuck. The prayers drove the spook away for a while but when it came back it was crueller than ever. It slapped my face so hard it left a big red mark.

It started throwing sticks and stones at us kids as we walked to school each day. The boys treated it more like a game. They picked up the stones, marked them and threw them back. The same stones were thrown again.

We were becoming so famous that General Andrew Jackson called round to see the spook for himself. He brought some kind of spirit expert with him. He reached the house some time in the afternoon. When he was half a mile away his carriage stopped and refused to budge. The Witch's voice told him it would appear for him that night in the house.

Now the spook had never appeared for any of us before. But that night we heard footsteps and saw a shadowy shape walking towards us. I buried my face in Ma's dress. The Witch-hunter fired at the shadow with a silver bullet.

He missed, of course . . . and he sure made a fine mess of our front window. The spook became wilder than ever. It slapped the man around the head and drove him out of the house.

We told James Johnson about the new trouble and he came up with another idea. "If it went away when we prayed, then it must be able to hear us. If it can hear us, it may be able to talk to us."

"Why would we want to talk to it?" Ma asked.

"Find out what it wants. Find out what we have to do to make it leave in peace."

Sounded like a good idea at the time. But we didn't know the trouble we were letting ourselves in for.

At first, the Witch began to answer our questions with whistles. Slowly it seemed to learn words. The whistles were broken up and started to form into whimpering sounds that were almost words. Finally we started to understand it.

Getting the Witch to talk was easy enough. Getting it to shut up was quite another matter! "Where are you from?" James Johnson asked it one night.

Back came the answer. *I am a spirit from everywhere, Heaven, Hell and Earth. I am in the air, in houses, in any place at any time. I have been created for millions of years. That is all that I will tell you.*

What we didn't know at first was that the Witch told lies. Every time we asked it questions it came up with a different answer. After it told us it was a million-year-old spirit, it changed its story. *I am the spirit of a person who was buried in the woods nearby. My grave has been disturbed. My bones are scattered. One of my teeth was lost under the house. I have been looking for that tooth.*

That sounded so sad. We'd heard of this sort of restless spirit. All we had to do was find the tooth, give it a Christian burial, and the Witch could rest in peace. The boys spent all day digging. We crawled under the porch till we were muddier than the hogs in the pen. That night the Witch laughed at us for being so foolish.

I will tell you the truth. I am the spirit of an early settler. I brought a large sum of money with me. I buried it for safety in the ground. I died before I could dig it up again. I have returned to tell you that it is hidden below your house. I want young Betsy to have that treasure.

The Witch didn't say why it wanted me to have the money. The boys dug again – this time they took up the floorboards. In the half-wrecked house the Witch returned and sighed. *You never learn, do you? This time I will tell you the truth. I am the spirit of old Kate Batts. Jack Bell (that was Pa) has done me a great wrong. I will not rest until he is in his grave. Be sure that I will drive him there.*

Old Kate Batts was a bad-tempered, loud-voiced, foul-mouthed woman. Being haunted by her would be a real problem. There was only one thing wrong with this spook story – Old Kate Batts was still alive and living just a few miles down the road! Kate was often heard to swear – and she was also heard to recite from the Bible. That's what the Witch began to do! In fact it amazed people because it could repeat the preacher's Sunday sermon word-for-word an hour after he'd given it in church.

After that the Witch seemed to turn its spite from me to Pa. I was near seventeen by this time and started to court Joshua Gardner from the next farm. *Don't marry him, Betsy*, the Witch pleaded with me. To tell the truth I was too young to marry him anyway, but the Witch went on and on about it. When I refused it gave me punches and slaps and fainting fits. Every time Joshua came to visit it screamed at him to leave me alone!

He left all right. No one could put up with those sorts of threats.

But while it was determined to look after me, it was carrying on a real fight to the death with Pa. He took to his sick bed and the Witch laughed. *He'll never get out of that bed alive.*

The doctor gave Pa all kinds of pills and medicines. None of them worked. On the morning of 19 December 1820 we couldn't wake Pa up. My brother, Williams, rushed to the medicine cabinet and found a bottle with a smoky liquid in it. The bottle was two-thirds empty. Williams rushed off for the doctor while Ma and me tried to wake Pa. That's when the voice cackled and told us, *It's useless to try to wake him up. I've got him this time!*

"What was in that bottle?" Ma shrieked.

Poison. I put it in the cabinet. I gave old Jack a big dose last night while he was fast asleep. That fixed him. It fixed him good.

By the time the doctor arrived Pa was dead. The bottle wasn't one of his medicines. "Bring me a saucer of milk," he said after he'd sniffed at it.

I fetched a saucer and he placed it on the floor. One of the cats came and started to drink it. The doctor placed a couple of drops of the liquid in the milk. The cat kept on drinking. When the saucer was empty it walked away. It leaned against the leg of a chair and slid down to the floor. The poor animal gave a couple of twitches of its legs then went stiff.

"Poison," the doctor said. Then he did something people have said was pretty stupid. He threw the bottle onto the fire and destroyed it.

"Are you satisfied?" I asked the Witch. It didn't reply. But at the funeral the next day we heard it cackling in the air as we stood around the grave. Then it began to sing its favourite drinking song! *Row me up some brandy-o!*

We were terrified of what that spirit would do next. But it seemed the worst was over. We hardly heard from it in the two weeks after Pa's funeral. It was only when I got the nerve to see Joshua Gardner that the Witch started getting violent with me again. Joshua left. This time he never came back.

Then one evening, a few months after Pa died, a black cannonball of some kind came down the chimney and it burst into a cloud of smoke. Out of the smoke came the Witch's voice. *I am going now. I will be gone for seven years. Goodbye to all!*

I wasn't there seven years later when it did come back. By then I was married to Dick Powell and living away from home. Ma and three of the boys did say there were noises and some bed-clothes pulled off. My brother John even said he heard the Witch announce she'd be back in a hundred and seven years. That'll be 1934, I reckon.

I won't be around to see that, of course. Like I say, I'm eighty-three now and I've seen enough of spooks to last me the rest of my life.

But I'll tell you one thing. I'm glad I met the family Witch. For me it proves there is some kind of after-life. When you're my age that becomes pretty important.

The Bell Witch — Facts

1. Betsy Bell repeated her story many times during her life. Her story was published by the haunted Jack Bell's great-grandson in 1934. She finally died at the age of eighty-three. But can her word be trusted? The writer, Charles, was relying on the stories of a very old woman. And, after all, she was at the centre of all the haunting and could have known more about it than she wanted to say. For example, some investigators suggested that she hated her father and she was the one who poisoned him, not some Witch-spirit. Betsy Bell was not the best witness.

2. Another source of the Bell Witch story is a full-length book by Betsy's brother, Williams. He made notes on the story twenty-six years after it happened. He never intended it to be published. Then, in 1891, his son Allen found it and handed it over to a writer who worked on it and published it. The fashion in those days was for dramatic titles – the writer, M. V. Ingram certainly gave his readers one! The book was called "An authenticated history of the famous Bell Witch. The wonder of the 19th century, an unexplained phenomenon of the Christian era. The mysterious talking goblin that terrorised the West end of Robertson County, Tennessee, tormenting John Bell to his death. The story of Betsy Bell, her lover and the haunting Sphinx". But Williams Bell was only

six when the haunting started. How accurately does a six-year-old remember things, especially when he waits till he is thirty-two before writing the tale? And Ingram never spoke to the man who made the notes.

3. A third source of information is the story as it was passed on by word of mouth. That shows remarkable changes from Betsy's and Williams' accounts. One version says:

• Jack Bell was a slave owner in North Carolina who killed his slave-master in a fight. He was tried but released when he claimed that he shot the man in self-defence.
• He moved to Tennessee but was plagued by bad luck and haunted by the ghost of the man he had killed.
• Jack's oldest daughter, Mary, was bothered by bad dreams and a ghost who appeared in her mirror and spoke to her.
• The ghost asked if it could marry Mary. The family refused. Mary fell ill and died.
• At her funeral a huge black bird appeared in the sky. It carried a bell around its neck that rang with the saddest chime anyone has heard. The bird vanished but the bell can still be heard.

A totally different story goes like this;

• Jack Bell became engaged to a widow. Her name was Kate Batts. She proved to have a terrible temper. Jack tried to break off the engagement. Kate

Batts refused.

- One day Kate Batts fell and knocked herself out. Bell thought she was dead so he locked her in the cellar of the farmhouse. Kate awoke and called to him for help. Ignoring her cries, he left her to starve.

- Bell married another woman and moved to Tennessee. They were soon haunted by a terrible black bird with a foul smell. In the house, noises were heard that kept the family awake.

- The ghost of Kate Batts appeared to the family. One night it announced that it had poisoned Bell. Next morning he was found dead.

- The figure of a dark-haired woman flying across the Bell farm was seen. It was last reported in 1980.

4. Some investigators have tried to take Betsy's story as fact and sought to explain it. They claim that Betsy was the centre of a poltergeist force. It was her uncontrolled power that made the noises and created the voices. Betsy hated her father and made his life a misery – not deliberately, perhaps. He was a gloomy and deeply religious man. He felt he was guilty of sins against heaven. The "Witch" was a punishment against him. The guilt made him ill until he was finally poisoned – by Betsy, perhaps . . . or maybe he swallowed the poison himself. The doctor's destruction of the bottle before it could be tested is also a strange event. Why would he do that? Was he trying to protect someone? Who?

5. Witch stories were taken seriously in the United States of America a hundred years or more before

the Bell Witch was heard of. In Salem, Massachusetts, the story of Hannah Glover is a typical one from that period:

- *John Goodwin's family were quite rich and content in their fine home. Then the spiteful eldest daughter accused a maid of stealing her clothes. The maid was sacked and went home to her mother . . . Hannah Glover.*
- *Even her husband swore that Hannah Glover was a witch. When her jobless daughter came home Hannah Glover set out for revenge. She made a doll from rags and sticks and held it over the smoking fire in her lowly shack.*
- *The spiteful Goodwin girl woke the whole house with her gurgling screams the next day. Soon the other children were affected by strange fits. Their mouths opened, then snapped shut fiercely. Their necks went slack and their heads rolled until they suddenly jerked up stiffly and painfully. They screamed with agony.*
- *A priest cured the youngest girl who described how she'd been possessed by demons. The magistrates were informed and discovered that Hannah Glover held a grudge against the Goodwin family. Hannah Glover was told to recite the Lord's Prayer – if she failed it would prove she was a witch. She failed and announced instead: "The Prince of Darkness will watch over me."*
- *Hannah Glover squeezed the throat of the rag doll she was carrying. The eldest Goodwin girl screamed that she was being choked to death. The doll was*

taken away from her and the child recovered. But Hannah Glover was sentenced to death.

- *Before she died the "witch" promised that there were others on Earth who would continue the Goodwin family torment. Sure enough, for several months after her death the children suffered nightmares and fits.*

- *Modern doctors believe that the Goodwin children were the victims of their own imaginations – a phenomenon known as hysteria. The Bell family would have read about Hannah Glover and the subsequent Salem Witch Trial. Did Betsy Bell suffer from a wild imagination and cause "hysteria" for her family?*

6. Watery Grave

We call the world we live in Earth . . . yet in fact it is mostly sea! It is no surprise that so many strange things happen at sea. For example, people and ships are said to disappear without trace in the Bermuda Triangle. And the sea has ghosts of its own that are every bit as strange as those on land . . .

Glasgow, Scotland – 1954

Rain fell from a colourless sky. Still the young man stood on the doorstep of the house and hesitated. His hair was cropped short and the water ran off it down his neck and face. A well-tanned, healthy face. But at this moment the expression was a worried one.

People passing in the street looked at him with suspicion. He had to go ahead or go back. He couldn't stand here any longer. He pressed the doorbell and waited.

The door opened an inch or two. "Who's that?" a

69

woman's voice asked.

"I'm looking for someone called . . . Keddie. Mrs Aileen Keddie?"

"Who wants her?" the voice asked.

"She doesn't know me," the young man said. "My name is Nigel Graham. She won't have heard of me before."

"What do you want?"

"I have to know if there's a Mrs Aileen Keddie living here," he said miserably.

"There might be. Depends what you want."

"I want to talk about her husband."

"He's dead."

"So, Mrs Keddie does live here, then?"

"She might."

"It involves money. Maybe a lot of money," he said, lowering his voice. "Money" was the magic word that opened the door a little wider. The woman's face was the unhealthy colour of rice pudding and her hair lank, grey and uncombed.

"Whose money?"

"It belonged to Mrs Keddie's husband," the young man explained.

The woman's rough hand shot forward, grabbed his wrist and drew him into the dingy hallway. "I'm Mrs Keddie. Where's the money?"

The hallway smelt of stale cabbage, cigarette smoke and cats. "Can we go inside, Mrs Keddie, and I'll explain. It's a strange story."

"Tea?" she said suddenly as she led him into a cluttered living room. A plastic-covered settee was in front of an old television set with a tiny screen.

Unwashed plates with scraps of stale food were being picked at by cats. The man didn't like to think what her tea would be like.

"No . . . thank you," he said.

"Please yourself," she said and sat in an armchair. She nodded for him to sit on the settee. "What's this all about, then?" she asked.

"I'm Nigel Graham," he began. "I've just come back from the Pacific."

"That's where my Jamie died."

The young man nodded. "I thought it might be," he confirmed.

"You mean you don't know?" she asked sharply. "You know about his money but you don't know about his dying? What sort of trick are you trying to pull?"

"Nothing! Nothing," he assured her. He chewed his lower lip unhappily. Then he spoke suddenly in a rush. "Look, I don't expect you to believe this but I think I may have met the ghost of your husband."

The woman narrowed her eyes. "I can believe it," she said. "My mother had second sight. She told me that Jamie would try to get in touch with me. I just didn't expect it to come from a young man like you."

Nigel Graham relaxed. "I left the army last year and decided I needed a break before I settled down to a job. An old army pal, Richard, and I decided to travel round the world together," he began. She watched him in silence so he went on. "We crossed the Atlantic to the States, then hitched across America to the west coast. We hadn't much money, so we signed on to be deck hands on an old steamship heading for Australia. And, believe me it was old."

"Don't worry, laddie, I've seen them on the Clyde. Jamie sailed in many an old rust bucket. The owners didn't care."

"That's what Richard and I said, but we sailed anyway. We were way out in the Pacific when we were woken up by cries of 'All hands on deck!' You wouldn't believe the way a fire had taken hold. We were carrying grain – not very explosive, but the fire was in the engine room. Once it reached the fuel tanks it would blow the old ship apart. The crew were good. They said they'd fight the fire. We were not going to be much help, they reckoned, so they jammed lifebelts onto us and lowered us over the side. If the fire was put under control they'd pick us up at first light. If it didn't . . . well, we didn't have time to discuss it. We swam as fast and as far as we could. We were well clear when the ship went up in a sheet of flame."

He paused for a moment as he remembered it. "They were good men, Mrs Keddie."

"Aye," she said quietly. For a few moments she shared his sadness.

He sniffed and went on. "The next day it was raining. We drifted and caught the rain water in our mouths. It would keep us alive a little longer, we reckoned. There just didn't seem much point. We were hundreds of miles from the nearest inhabited island. Sooner or later the sharks would get us. It was a hopeless situation. Richard and I talked about diving deep down and drowning rather than face that slow death."

"Aye," the woman nodded. "I know a lot of sailors who never even learned to swim."

"The rain stopped and the sun burned us. I thought I was beginning to have hallucinations when I heard a steady splashing. It was just like the sound of someone rowing. When I looked up and saw a lifeboat heading towards us I knew I was dreaming. The man was a seaman. He had a dark blue sweater and black trousers. He pulled us aboard and we collapsed in the bottom of his boat." Nigel looked up at the woman and said, "He told us his name was . . . James Keddie."

Mrs Keddie just nodded. "Brown hair going thin, side whiskers, a tooth missing at the front?"

The young man nodded. "We tried to ask him where he was from but he wouldn't tell us. Only that his ship had sunk in a storm and that he'd been rowing ever since."

"That's my Jamie," the woman said suddenly vicious. "A black-hearted liar!"

"He could have been . . . "

"Don't mind me. Carry on," she ordered.

"We wondered how long he'd survived without food or water. He reached into the sea and pulled out a fish. When he split it open he showed us how to suck water from the flesh and then eat it. It saved our lives without a doubt. But he wouldn't eat or drink anything himself."

"No, he wouldn't," Aileen Keddie said quietly.

"Before nightfall we sighted an island. A tiny rock in the sea, really, but there was fresh rain-water in pools and fish so tame we could just lift them out of the water with our bare hands. James still wouldn't eat. He just kept saying, 'Two lives saved makes up for our two lives lost.' When we asked him what he meant he wouldn't explain. He just kept saying, 'Two lives saved makes up for two lives lost.'"

"That would be right," the woman said.

"He also said, 'Aileen should have the money.'"

She looked up. "And he told you where it was?"

"Before he left. He set off in the rowing boat that night. He said he'd tell the Coastguard service where to find us. We'd be rescued in forty-eight hours. He only asked us to do one thing for him . . . he asked us to contact you and give you a message. He made me write down your address, and a number. He said the number was of a bank safe-deposit box. Here it is," Nigel said and passed a slip of paper across to her.

"I'll need a key," she said.

"He told me you'll find it in the coal shed under a loose brick."

The woman stood up, said, "Wait here," and hurried out of the door. Two minutes later she returned more slowly. In her blackened hands she held a small key.

"You did well," she said.

"I'm pleased you found it. I don't understand it – I'm not even sure I believe what's happened. There's just one thing, Mrs Keddie, I'd like in return . . ."

"A share of the treasure! Is that it?" she said and clutched the key close to her chest.

"No, no, Mrs Keddie. You husband gave me my life. That's reward enough. The Coastguard was there within two days to pick us up. They had a report that a man in a rowing boat had hailed a ship. Told the crew our position and asked them to radio for help. That had to be your husband. I don't want a reward. No . . . I'd just like you to tell me about your husband."

The woman relaxed and wiped her coal-smeared hands on her greasy apron. "He was a villain," she said. "Every time he came back from a trip he brought something extra with him. A watch or two, a piece of jewellery maybe. He sold them in the quayside pubs."

"He was a smuggler?"

"Not big time, you know. Just a little each trip. He was never greedy. That's how he got away with it. But over the years the money must have mounted up. God knows he spent precious little on me. All he did buy was his beer."

"You never knew where he kept it?"

"He'd never tell me. He thought he'd go on a trip, one day, and come back to find I'd emptied his little treasure chest."

"He should have trusted you . . .," Nigel began.

The woman threw back her head, cackled loudly and showed her cracked and yellowed teeth. "Steal his money! Ha! Of course I'd have stolen his money. He knew exactly what I'd do!"

Nigel nodded. "He's dead, isn't he?" he said.

"He's dead."

"I'm sorry."

"Don't be. His death wasn't the real tragedy. The sadness was that he didn't tell me where he'd left his money . . . and the sadness was that he took two good

75

men with him to their deaths."

Nigel's face cleared a little. "That's why he kept saying, 'Two lives saved makes up for two lives lost.'"

"That's right. It was eight years ago. I guess his miserable spirit hasn't been able to rest since he died. He just had to save two lives to make up for his stupidity." The woman shivered, leaned forward and picked up one of the cats to hug for a little warmth in the damp and gloomy room.

"The captain wrote me a letter. He said that the crew were called on deck because of a storm that was brewing up. Jamie was reported drunk and had to be dragged from his bunk. He broke free of two officers and ran for a lifeboat. He was shouting that a hurricane was on its way and it would sink them . . . he couldn't swim, of course. So he panicked and he tried to launch the lifeboat. The officers made another attempt to grab him. The boat swung loose and all three fell into the sea with the lifeboat. They all drowned." Then she added bitterly, "You see, it wasn't just his own death that was a tragedy. It was the waste of those two innocent officers. What a thing to weigh your soul down as you try to climb to heaven. You didn't meet a ghost, Mr Graham . . . you met a lost soul from Hell."

"There wasn't any chance that he survived?" Nigel asked.

"No. They found all three bodies and dragged them out for a proper burial at sea. The only thing that was missing was the lifeboat," she said.

The two sat in silence for a long while. The only sounds were the purr of the cat and the steady patter of rain against the window. Nigel Graham rose slowly to his feet. "I hope you have some happiness with the money," he said quietly.

The woman didn't seem to hear him. "I think he's paid his debt to those two officers now. I think his poor wandering soul will find some peace at last."

"I hope so," the young man said. He stepped into the dank hall, pulled up his collar and walked out into the fresh evening air.

Watery Grave – Facts

1. As with most ghost stories there are several possible explanations. Perhaps Nigel and Richard did suffer from heat stroke and hallucinate about the ghostly rescue. (Two people seeing the same hallucination is not uncommon.) The radio operator on their burning ship would have sent a message as to their position. After two days of searching the coastguards could well have found the survivors without any ghostly help.

2. Nigel's knowing about the "ghost's" wife, her address, the location of the key and the number of the bank account also has to be explained. That is harder. James Keddie may have told someone of the hidden money before he died – then Nigel Graham made up the story about the ghost in order to get a share of that money. Otherwise a supernatural explanation seems the most likely in this case!

3. There is little doubt that Mrs Keddie would believe the story of her husband's ghost. Sailors are among the most superstitious people in the world. They believe that the supernatural is present in many of the things they do or say. A mistake could send the sailor – or even the whole crew – to disaster.
   One of the curious beliefs of sailors was that they should never set sail on a Friday. This came from early Christian times because Christ died on a Friday.

*The superstition may sound silly. It was certainly a
nuisance to the British Royal Navy in the nineteenth
century. They decided to "prove" that Friday was no
different from any other day by building a "Friday"
ship.*

* *The shipyard began building the new warship on a
Friday*
* *The ship was named HMS* Friday
* *The ship was launched on a Friday*
* *The ship set off on its first voyage on a Friday*
* *HMS* Friday *and her crew disappeared and were
never seen again!*

4. *Sailors have faced death for thousands of years.
Over that time they have learned that some things
seem to bring them luck – others bad luck.*

Unlucky . . .
* *A black travelling bag for a sailor*
* *Meeting someone with red hair on your way to the
ship*
* *Meeting someone with flat feet*
* *Stepping on board with your left foot first*
* *Seeing a curlew or a cormorant when sailing*
* *Losing a bucket or mop overboard*
* *Having flowers on board a ship – because they could
be the sign of a funeral*
* *Throwing stones over the side of a ship – the small
ripples may turn to big waves before your journey is
finished*
* *Wearing the clothes of a dead sailor*
* *Saying the word "drown" while at sea*

Lucky . . .

- *Black cats*
- *Seeing a swallow when at sea*
- *Killing a seagull or an albatross (because these birds carry the souls of dead sailors)*
- *Pouring wine on the deck before sailing – from the custom of giving gifts of food and wine to the ancient gods*
- *Sighting a porpoise at sea*
- *Placing a silver coin under the masthead before sailing – another gift to the gods, perhaps*

7. Beware Ticonderoga!

What would you do if a ghost asked you to kill someone it hated? You would refuse, wouldn't you? But what if your refusal meant that the ghost would turn its hatred on you! You are in an impossible position. Kill or be killed. That was the choice facing the Scottish Lord of Inverawe 250 years ago ...

Fort Carillon, Canada – 1758

They wore red coats so they wouldn't show the blood. Of course, the British soldiers hoped it would be the blood of the enemy: the French.

General Abercromby rapped on the dinner table with a spoon. The officers lowered their forks and turned towards their leader. He cleared his throat. "Gentlemen! Tomorrow we attack Fort Carillon. I am sure that we will all enjoy the attack ... especially as the French have less than four thousand men to our sixteen thousand."

The officers sat in the sawmill two miles from the Fort. It was their headquarters. They laughed at the thought of tomorrow's easy victory. The General went on, "Of course it would be foolish for us to suggest the French will turn tail and run away. I'm sure they will fight bravely. But never forget, it is our duty to take the Fort. If a few Frenchmen get hurt in the process then that's just their bad luck, isn't it gentlemen?"

There were murmurs of agreement. At the back of the room Major William Anderson turned to his friend, Lord Inverawe, and murmured, "That's what they said before the Battle of Monongahela three years ago. Look what happened there!"

"It was a massacre," Inverawe nodded. His long grey hair was combed back from his handsome face and he played with his table knife while he waited for the General to finish his speech. "Old fool," he yawned.

"Any questions?" the General announced.

A young captain in a tartan kilt of the Blackwatch Regiment stood up. "Excuse me, General, but our scouts report that the French have cut down all of the trees in front of Fort Carillon. They've built a high wall with musket loopholes to fire through. Will we use our cannon to knock a few holes in this wall?"

The General picked up his pipe and began to fill it slowly. "With so many men I don't think it is worth unloading the cannon from the boats. There will be no bombardment."

"He may regret that," Major Anderson whispered.

"No, he won't. He'll be sitting here smoking his

82

pipe. We are the ones who will regret it. We'll be the ones fighting."

The young Blackwatch officer was persisting with his questions. "Apart from the wall, the French have left the branches in front of the wall. We'll be tangled in them, whether we're on horses or on foot. We'll make easy targets for their muskets. Couldn't we attack the sides of the Fort?"

"Front, back or sides," General Abercromby smiled. "Makes no difference. We will win tomorrow."

"But . . ." the young man began.

The General leaned forward in irritation. He pointed the stem of his pipe at the man. "Scared, Captain?"

The officer turned as red as the uniform jackets and sat down. General Abercromby smiled and picked up a glass of wine. "Gentlemen, I wish to propose a toast." His officers picked up their glasses and rose to their feet. "Tomorrow night we shall be dining in Fort Carillon. Here's to . . . no! I hate that French name. When we have captured it we will change the name back to the old Indian name. So, Gentlemen, here is to Fort Ticonderoga!"

From the back of the room came a cry of pain and terror. This was followed by a crash of plates and glasses. Lord Inverawe had fallen forward onto his table in a dead faint. His red coat shone brilliantly in the lamplight like a bloodstain on the tablecloth.

They carried Lord Inverawe to his tent where the surgeon examined him. "His pulse is very weak," he said quietly.

"What's wrong with him?" Major Anderson asked.

"His skin is pale with a fine film of sweat. I would say he has suffered a massive shock. Sleep is best. He will awake. When he does, give him brandy to revive him," the doctor ordered.

Major Anderson pulled a stool to the bedside where he sat watching his friend. After half an hour Inverawe's eyes flickered, then opened. He looked around the tent and back at Anderson. "Sorry about this, Anderson," he said.

His friend helped him to sit up in bed and let him sip the brandy. "How do you feel?"

Lord Inverawe gave a faint smile. "What does it matter? Tomorrow I die."

"Oh, come along!" Anderson cried. "I know the General's plan has its weaknesses, but . . ."

"No. I will die tomorrow. I have known for more than ten years that I would die at Ticonderoga. I never knew where the place was until the General announced it tonight. Sorry for making such a fool of myself."

"You must have a reason," Major Anderson said quietly. "Care to tell me about it?"

The Scottish Lord closed his eyes and said, "It began one stormy night in my Scottish castle . . ." He stopped and his eyes crinkled with a smile. "It sounds like the start of every ghost story you ever heard, doesn't it?"

"Go on," his friend urged.

"I was writing by the fireside late at night. A servant came in and said there was a man at the door, asking for shelter. You know about Highland customs. We never refuse shelter to anyone . . . and once we've offered it we never take it away. It doesn't matter who the visitor is."

"So. Who was he?"

"A Highlander in the McDonald tartan. He was soaked through. Clearly he'd been riding all night. Now he was exhausted and desperate to rest. I never asked where he'd been or where he was going, of course. If he wanted to tell me he would be welcome to. I offered him a dry kilt and he thanked me. Then he saw the tartan – our Campbell family tartan – and suddenly changed his mind. It was as if it was the Devil's own kilt! He seemed afraid of it and said he would simply retire to bed and leave in the morning. Then he asked for some water to clean himself before he went to bed. I ordered my servant to help him. Then I went back to my writing."

"You think he may have been some kind of outlaw?"

"I soon found out he was more sinister than he seemed. The servant knocked on my door timidly and asked if he could have a word. He had removed the washing bowl from the stranger's room . . . and found the water stained with blood."

"He was wounded?" Anderson asked.

"That's what I thought at first. That could have explained his wild appearance. I thought he'd been attacked and escaped. Of course, that didn't explain why he was unwilling to talk. I was too stupid to see the truth!"

His friend nodded. "He hadn't been attacked and

that wasn't his blood. He was the attacker and the blood came from his victim? He was a fugitive and he didn't want to risk your betraying him."

"Exactly! What I didn't know was the name of his victim. I found that out in the strangest way." He sipped at the brandy again and went on. "I retired to my bed soon after midnight and the wind was tearing at the shutters of the room. Suddenly they smashed open. My candle was blown out. All I could see in the darkness was a glow."

"Moonlight?"

"The storm clouds were too thick to allow in any natural light. This was a light from hell. The glow steadily formed itself into a shape. I began to make out a man. Then I could see that the man had half of his clothes slashed away from his body. The body was covered in bloody wounds." Lord Inverawe shuddered at the memory. "I've seen men die in war but this sight was more horrible than anything I've ever seen on the battlefield. I knew at once this man was dead. I was seeing a ghost."

"I've heard that such things haunt old castles like yours," Anderson nodded.

"Ah, but this ghost hadn't come to haunt the castle – it had come to haunt me!" the lord insisted. "The figure took a step towards my bed. Under the dreadful wounds on its head I could make out his face at last. It was no stranger to me. It was the face of my cousin, Donald Campbell."

"You imagined it was your dead cousin," I suppose, Anderson said soothingly.

"I didn't know he was dead!" Inverawe said. "I

didn't hear that news until two days later!"

"What did the ghost want?" Major Anderson asked.

"Revenge. What else?"

"Did he name his killer?"

Lord Inverawe gave a sudden laugh. "He didn't have to. He cried out to me, Inverawe! Inverawe! Blood has been shed! Do not shield my murderer! I knew at once that the man who had killed Donald was in my castle! And Donald's ghost was asking me to betray him! You see my problem?"

"Yes," Anderson admitted. "You had a duty to avenge your cousin – but you had a duty to your guest. What a choice!"

"I refused to make that choice at first. I slammed the shutters closed and took a fresh candle from the corridor. The ghost vanished in the light of that candle and I felt safe. But three more times that night Donald's ghost appeared. Three more times I refused to help him. I tried promising I'd help once he had left the protection of my castle, but not while he slept under my roof. That final time Donald screamed at me, Farewell, Inverawe, farewell. Until we meet again . . . at Ticonderoga! Then he was gone."

Anderson gripped his friend's arm. "It was a bad dream. You were reminded of it when General Abercromby mentioned the name of the Fort," he said.

The man in the bed shook his head. "How can you remember something you've never known?" he asked. "For the last ten years I have searched books and questioned travellers. Have you heard of a place called Ticonderoga? No one knew the name – and I had no idea I had arrived here until tonight. Donald's ghost was right. I have arrived at Ticonderoga. I also know he wants revenge – not on his killer, now – but on me! The man who sheltered my cousin's murderer."

Major Anderson said, "The doctor has left a sleeping draft. Drink it and get some rest. Tomorrow night, after the battle, we'll be drinking your health, you'll see. I'll stay here the night."

But there was no rest for the men that night. Lord Inverawe woke in the darkest, quietest hour and screamed at the shadows at the bottom of his bed. Major Anderson sat up quickly, picked up a loaded pistol and pointed it towards the doorway. The tent flap trembled but no shape appeared. "What did you see?" Anderson asked as dawn light trickled through the canvas walls.

"I saw Donald," the Lord said weakly. "Still covered in blood . . . and saying he would meet me on the battlefield."

"Don't go," Anderson said simply.

"I must. If I don't go, then he will find some other way to bring about my death. Pass me my uniform my friend. I will fight and I will die. It will be a blessed relief from the nightmares."

The French waited for the British to attack. They smiled as Abercromby's army walked into the tangle of trees. They cheered as their musketeers picked off the redcoats one at a time.

But the French looked with fear as a British

commander raced into the storm of musket fire as if he was driven by a devil. Perhaps he was. Horses fell and died on the sharp stakes the defenders had hidden in front of their walls. Redcoats fell wounded and died in the tangled branches. Still that British commander led the attacks.

After five hours of wasted life Abercromby ordered the British to withdraw. Weary men trooped back to the camp by the sawmill – sixteen thousand men driven off by four thousand.

Only one of those men seemed quietly cheerful. The commander – Lord Inverawe. "The curse has been lifted," he said to his friend Major Anderson that night.

"Cousin Donald had a change of heart," Anderson nodded. "In fact he must have protected you! A slight tear in your sleeve from a musket shot. Otherwise not a scratch."

Inverawe smiled for the first time that day. "Just a slight graze under that tear – the red coat doesn't show the blood."

"Better have it seen to," Anderson advised.

"It can wait," the Lord shrugged. "Pass the brandy."

So they waited till they had finished the brandy. They waited till they had slept off the weariness of the battle. They waited until the seriously wounded men had been treated.

Finally Inverawe went to the doctor. "A scratch, doctor."

"Even scratches can kill," the tired doctor sighed. "You should have come to me earlier."

"I was too busy celebrating," Inverawe laughed.

"You are more cheerful today after your gloom before the battle."

Inverawe nodded. "I am a man who was sentenced to death – then granted a pardon on the scaffold," he joked.

As he pulled on the red coat he said, "Thank you, doctor. That should do it."

A week later the wound turned swollen and painful. Two days after that the doctor had to amputate the arm. But the poison was in his blood. The next day Lord Inverawe fell into a fever. His eyes fixed on a spot somewhere in the air and he cried, "I hear you, Donald! I hear you! Shield not a murderer!"

On 18 July, 1753 Lord Inverawe died at Ticonderoga . . . just as he had said he would.

Beware Ticonderoga! — Facts

The battle was recorded by a historian named Parkman. His story backed up the tale told by Inverawe's friends. Parkman wrote, "With the Highlanders of the 42nd Brigade was Major Campbell of Inverawe. He seemed silent and gloomy in the midst of the generally cheerful men. His soul was dark with a vision of his own death."

Any soldier going into battle must fear that he will die. Among 16,000 men there must have been many who thought that this would be the day of their death – many of those were right.

Lord Inverawe could well have had a nightmare on the night that cousin Donald died. The name Ticonderoga could have been a half-remembered name from that dream.

On the other hand, there are so many reports of ghosts appearing to relatives close to their time of death that the possibility of Donald appearing has to be taken seriously. A few examples are . . .

1. *In 1957* Fate *magazine recorded a typical case. Mary Travers was waiting for her husband to come home from work one evening. She heard a cab draw up outside the door, heard her husband's voice call "Good night!" to the cab driver, then heard his footsteps approach the front door. She went into the hall to meet him. Mrs Travers was in time to see him close the door and turn to face her. His face was a blank, white mask. She screamed with horror*

and neighbours came running. By the time they arrived the phantom had vanished. A few minutes later the telephone rang. It was the police, calling to say that Mr Travers had died in a train crash on his way from the office.

2. *Not all "point-of-death" experiences are visions – or even horrific. In 1975 a young man left home to play football. He knew his father was ill in hospital – he didn't know how ill. The football match kicked off at one o'clock. After an hour the young man had a strange experience. He headed towards the goal and everyone on the pitch seemed to freeze. He kept going while the opposition simply watched. He kicked the ball towards the goal . . . he kicked it very badly, yet the ball floated over the helpless goalkeeper and into the net. The boy's father was proud of his football skills but had always been too busy working to actually watch his son. When the boy arrived home there was a message for him to contact the hospital. His father had died at the exact time he scored his strange goal.*

3. *And not all feelings are entirely accurate. There is a story of a woman from Newcastle-upon-Tyne. In the late 1890s she went out shopping. Suddenly she had a great feeling of sadness. She "knew" that something terrible had happened to her husband. Yet he returned home safely that evening . . . with the news that an orphan child they had cared for had died that afternoon!*

4. *The experience of sensing a death seems to be as much to do with the person feeling it as it is to do with the dying person. In 1846 a "Medium" called Daniel Dunglas-Home saw a vision of a friend. The vision gave a signal that meant "three". Home knew this meant his friend had died three days before. He was right. But Home is unusual in that a point-of-death vision happened to him more than once. He also saw his mother's ghost before he received news of her death.*

5. *Lord Inverawe heard as well as saw his cousin Donald. That too has been recorded in other cases. A Finnish woman awoke one morning to see her half-brother standing at the end of her bed. He told her that he had come to say goodbye. She later discovered that the half-brother had killed himself hundreds of miles away at the moment she saw his phantom.*

6. *There are many more cases – too many to say whether it's a coincidence or it's a lie. Though there are a lot of frauds and mistakes in spook reports, you can never really say there are no such things as ghosts. Can you?*